ANNE GEDDES

Down in the Garden

BOOK OF DAYS

Cedco Publishing Company

ANNE GEDDES ™
ISBN 1-55912-020-7

© 1996 Anne Geddes

Published in 1996 by Cedco Publishing Company
2955 Kerner Blvd., San Rafael, CA 94901

Third Printing, December 1996

Designed by Jane Seabrook
Produced by Kel Geddes
Typeset by Image Design
Images first published in *Down in the Garden*.
Color separations by Image Centre
Printed by South China Printing Co. Ltd., Hong Kong

Please write to us for a FREE FULL COLOR catalog of our fine Anne Geddes calendars
and books, Cedco Publishing Company, 2955 Kerner Blvd., San Rafael, CA 94901.

Anne and Lilly

*"I am frequently asked why I photograph babies so often, and where my ideas come from.
Little babies are indeed my inspiration, and I can not imagine a photographic life without them
playing a major part in it. Where this special love for babies comes from I can not tell you,
and I have spent much time searching for an answer myself. All I know is that they are
perfect little human beings in their own way, and we should all take time to cherish
them, especially while they are very small."* Anne Geddes

These words are taken from the foreword to Anne's latest book,
Down in the Garden. They give an insight to the special magic that
Anne is able to create in her photographic works.

A visit to Anne's garden and her unique vision of all that is
beautiful is a journey that shouldn't be missed.

JANUARY

1

2

3

4

5

6

7

JANUARY

8

9

10

11

12

13

14

15

16

17

18

19

20

21

JANUARY

22

23

24

25

26

27

28

29

30

31

NOTES

F EBRUARY

1

2

3

4

5

6

7

FEBRUARY

8

9

10

11

12

13

14

15

16

17

18

19

20

21

FEBRUARY

22

23

24

25

26

27

28

NOTES

MARCH

1

2

3

4

5

6

7

MARCH

8

9

10

11

12

13

14

15

16

17

18

19

20

21

MARCH

22

23

24

25

26

27

28

29

30

31

NOTES

APRIL

1

2

3

4

5

6

7

APRIL

8

9

10

11

12

13

14

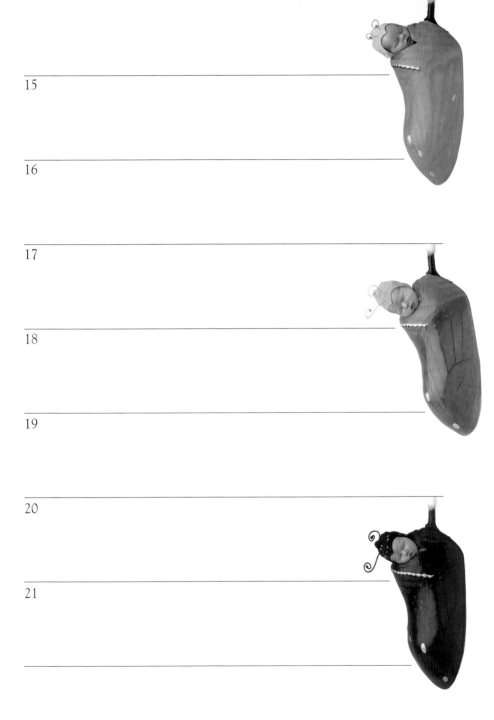

15

16

17

18

19

20

21

APRIL

22

23

24

25

26

27

28

29

30

NOTES

MAY

1 _____

2 _____

3 _____

4 _____

5 _____

6 _____

7 _____

_____

MAY

8

9

10

11

12

13

14

15

16

17

18

19

20

21

MAY

22

23

24

25

26

27

28

29

30

31

NOTES

JUNE

1

2

3

4

5

6

7

J UNE

8

9

10

11

12

13

14

15 _____

16 _____

17 _____

18 _____

19 _____

20 _____

21 _____

_____

J U N E

22

23

24

25

26

27

28

29

30

NOTES

JULY

1

2

3

4

5

6

7

JULY

8

9

10

11

12

13

14

15

16

17

18

19

20

21

JULY

22

23

24

25

26

27

28

29

30

31

NOTES

AUGUST

1

2

3

4

5

6

7

AUGUST

8

9

10

11

12

13

14

15 _____

16 _____

17 _____

18 _____

19 _____

20 _____

21 _____

A UGUST

22

23

24

25

26

27

28

29

30

31

NOTES

SEPTEMBER

1

2

3

4

5

6

7

SEPTEMBER

8

9

10

11

12

13

14

15

16

17

18

19

20

21

SEPTEMBER

22

23

24

25

26

27

28

29

30

NOTES

OCTOBER

1

2

3

4

5

6

7

OCTOBER

8

9

10

11

12

13

14

15

16

17

18

19

20

21

OCTOBER

22

23

24

25

26

27

28

29
_____

30
_____

31
_____

NOTES

NOVEMBER

1

2

3

4

5

6

7

NOVEMBER

8

9

10

11

12

13

14

15

16

17

18

19

20

21

November

22

23

24

25

26

27

28

29

30

NOTES

DECEMBER

1

2

3

4

5

6

7

DECEMBER

8

9

10

11

12

13

14

15

16

17

18

19

20

21

DECEMBER

22

23

24

25

26

27

28

29

30

31

NOTES

The

year

in

review...

JANUARY

FEBRUARY

MARCH

APRIL

MAY

JUNE

J ULY

A UGUST

SEPTEMBER

OCTOBER

November

December

Notes

NOTES